MAKING THE GRADE

Together

EASY POPULAR MIXED DUETS FOR FLUTE AND CLARINET
SELECTED AND ARRANGED BY LYNDA FRITH

Exclusive distributors:
Music Sales Limited
Newmarket Road, Bury St. Edmunds, Suffolk IP33 3YB.
This book © Copyright 1996 Chester Music.
Order No. CH61172
ISBN 0-7119-6143-3
Cover design by Pemberton & Whitefoord.
Printed in the United Kingdom by
Caligraving Limited, Thetford, Norfolk.

Chester Music

(A division of Music Sales Limited)
8/9 Frith Street, London W1V 5TZ.

INTRODUCTION

This collection of 17 popular duets has been carefully arranged to provide attractive repertoire for young flautists and clarinettists to play together. The technical standard of each part is equal, giving both players an opportunity to play the tune. The pieces are carefully graded, and should be suitable for players using the solo MAKING THE GRADE books 1 to 3.

CONTENTS

NIGHTS IN WHITE SATIN

Words & music by Justin Hayward

The tune starts in the flute part but then passes to the clarinet at bar 9.

Always be aware of who has the tune and adjust your dynamics accordingly.

SOMEWHERE OUT THERE

Words & music by James Horner, Barry Mann & Cynthia Weil

Work at the legato quavers in each part, making sure that there is no jerkiness.

TELL ME IT'S NOT TRUE

Words & music by Willy Russell

Notice the time signature changes and be sure to keep a steady crotchet beat.

HOW DEEP IS YOUR LOVE

Words & music by Barry Gibb, Robin Gibb & Maurice Gibb

There are a lot of syncopated rhythms in this piece, especially in the flute part.

Make sure you don't shorten the fourth count.

LOVE HURTS

Words & music by Boudleaux Bryant

The clarinet plays a gentle, legato accompaniment in this duet, while the flute takes the tune.

STREETS OF LONDON

Words & music by Ralph McTell

This piece sounds best if it is played in long phrases, so take plenty of breath,
and try to make each one last for four bars.

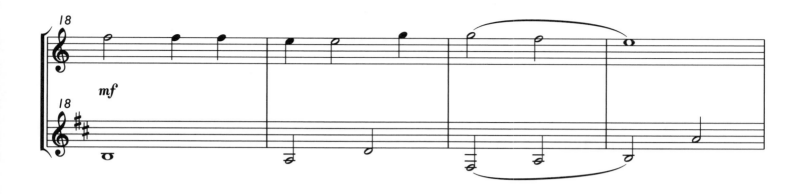

TO LOVE SOMEBODY

Words & music by Barry Gibb & Robin Gibb

The two parts are very independent, so be aware of what your partner is doing.

13

LOVE IS ALL AROUND

Words & music by Reg Presley

The two parts work together rhythmically for most of this piece.
Be careful to take the rests together as well.

TEARS IN HEAVEN

Words & music by Eric Clapton & Will Jennings

There needs to be a lot of sensitivity in the phrasing,
with tiny ups and downs in the dynamics of this gentle piece.

COULD IT BE MAGIC

Words & music by Barry Manilow & Adrienne Anderson

Don't be alarmed by the accidentals in the clarinet part at the beginning and end!

These bars are from Chopin's Prelude in C minor.

PENNY LANE

Words & music by John Lennon & Paul McCartney

The semiquavers in the flute part should not be rushed.

The clarinet will need to follow the flute part very carefully.

I WILL ALWAYS LOVE YOU

Words & music by Dolly Parton

The flute has the tune until the end of bar 14, when it takes the counter-melody.

The clarinet part needs to come through at this point.

23

AN ENGLISHMAN IN NEW YORK

Words & music by Sting

This music moves along at quite a pace. Start by practising fairly slowly,
making sure you play the syncopated rhythms correctly.

D.C. al Coda ⊕   **Coda** ⊕

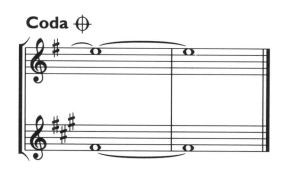

FERRY 'CROSS THE MERSEY

Words & music by Gerard Marsden

Try to feel the two minims in a bar as this will help you play the triplets in time.

WIRED FOR SOUND

Words & music by BA Robertson & Alan Tarney

There are several time signature changes here, so it is important to keep a steady crotchet beat throughout.

The flute needs to be especially aware of the beat provided by the clarinet from bar 21.

SON OF A PREACHER MAN

Words & music by John Hurley & Ronnie Wilkins

There are a great many repeated notes in both parts, so count carefully!

HE'S GOT THE WHOLE WORLD IN HIS HANDS

Traditional

This has a lively, bouncy feel to it.

It moves quite fast, so the clarinet will need to practise the triplets first.